Think Thinner, Snoopy

Selected Cartoons from
DON'T HASSLE ME WITH YOUR SIGHS,
CHUCK   Vol. 2

Charles M. Schulz

CORONET BOOKS
Hodder Fawcett, London.

Copyright © 1975 by United Features Syndicate, Inc.

First Published in the United States by
Fawcett Publications, Inc.

Coronet edition 1980

British Library C.I.P.

Schulz, Charles Monroe
  Think Thinner, Snoopy.
  I. Title
  741.5'973   PN6728.P4

  ISBN 0 340 25478 5

Printed in Great Britain for Hodder
Fawcett Ltd., Mill Road, Dunton Green,
Sevenoaks, Kent (Editorial Office: 47
Bedford Square, London, WC1 3DP) by
C. Nicholls & Company Ltd
The Philips Park Press, Manchester

**Also by the same author,
and available in Coronet Books:**

Keep Up The Good Work Charlie Brown
It's Show Time Snoopy
They're Playing Your Song, Charlie Brown
Play Ball Snoopy
Watch Out Charlie Brown
It's All Yours Snoopy
You Can't Win Them All Charlie Brown
You're So Smart Snoopy

※ SIGH ※

DO YOU KNOW ANY GOOD RULES FOR LIVING, CHUCK?

KEEP THE BALL LOW..

DON'T LEAVE YOUR CRAYONS IN THE SUN, USE DENTAL FLOSS EVERY DAY, GIVE FOUR WEEKS NOTICE WHEN ORDERING A CHANGE OF ADDRESS AND DON'T SPILL THE SHOE POLISH!

SUPPERTIME ISN'T FOR ANOTHER HALF HOUR

I WAS JUST HOPING FOR A FEW CELERY STICKS...

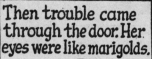

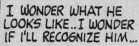

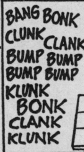

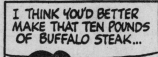

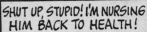

WHY DO BIRDS NEED SO MUCH STRING WHEN THEY'RE BUILDING A NEST?

I'M SURE I DON'T KNOW

IF IT'S JUST A MATTER OF LOOKING, I'VE LOOKED!

I'VE LOOKED FOR HAPPINESS AT HOME ≩ SIGH ≩

I'VE LOOKED ALL OVER THIS NEIGHBORHOOD FOR HAPPINESS...SOMEDAY, I'LL LOOK ALL OVER THIS COUNTRY FOR HAPPINESS...

BONK!

I KNEW IT WOULD HAPPEN...HIS KNEES ARE STARTING TO GO!

HE'S BEEN HITTING BALLS AGAINST THAT GARAGE FOR WEEKS...

HE'S PRACTICING FOR A MIXED-DOUBLES TOURNAMENT

OH? WHO'S GOING TO BE HIS PARTNER?

THE GARAGE!

SOMEDAY, WHEN A BOOK IS PUBLISHED ILLUSTRATING THE GREAT DINNERS OF ALL TIME, THIS DINNER WILL BE ON PAGE ONE!

THEN AGAIN, IT MAY NOT!

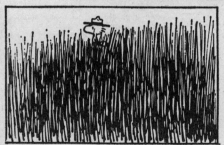

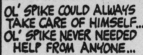

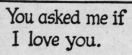

My darling,

You asked me if
I love you.

There is only one
thing I can say.

Yeah.

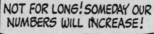

ALSO AVAILABLE FROM CORONET BOOKS

CHARLES M. SCHULZ

☐	24517 4	It's Show Time Snoopy	65p
☐	24499 2	Snoopy And The Red Baron	75p
☐	22951 9	Play Ball Snoopy	60p
☐	22304 9	That's Life Snoopy	60p
☐	21797 9	Watch Out Charlie Brown	60p
☐	19927 X	You're So Smart Snoopy	60p
☐	18303 9	There's No-one Like You Snoopy	60p
☐	17844 2	Take It Easy, Charlie Brown	60p
☐	10760 X	We're On Your Side, Charlie Brown	60p

JOHNNY HART

☐	18820 0	B.C. On The Rocks	60p
☐	19474 X	B.C. Right On	60p
☐	19873 7	B.C. Cave In	60p
☐	21248 9	B.C. Dip In The Road	60p

PARKER/RECHIN/WILDER

☐	23230 7	Crock	60p

All these books are available at your local bookshop or newsagents or can be ordered direct from the publisher. Just tick the titles you want and fill in the form below.

Prices and availability subject to change without notice.

CORONET BOOKS, P.O. Box 11, Falmouth, Cornwall.
Please send cheque or postal order, and allow the following for postage and packing:

U.K. – One book 30p plus 12p per copy for each additional book ordered, up to a maximum of £1.29

B.F.P.O. and EIRE – 30p for the first book plus 12p per copy for the next 5 books, thereafter 8p per book.

OTHER OVERSEAS CUSTOMERS – 50p for the first book and 15p per copy for each additional book.

Name ....

Address ....

....

Dear Spike,

Thank you for inviting me to have Thanksgiving dinner with you and the coyotes.

It sounds like fun. However....

How do I know the coyotes won't eat ME?